Easy Piano S▮▮▮▮s

C000151421

Jazz Standards

Bernie's Tune

Caravan

I Wish I Knew How It Would Feel To Be Free

Mood Indigo

It Don't Mean A Thing
(If It Ain't Got That Swing)

Pennies From Heaven

Tequila

Walkin' Shoes

Fly Me To The Moon (In Other Words)

East Of The Sun (And West Of The Moon)

Lullaby Of Birdland

Perdido

Lover Man (Oh Where Can You Be)

In A Sentimental Mood

Satin Doll

Stella By Starlight

You Brought A New Kind Of Love To Me

I'll Remember April

Blues Greats

Basin Street Blues

The Man I Love

Angel Eyes

Swingin' Shepherd Blues

Things Ain't What They Used To Be

Prelude No.2 from
Three Preludes for Piano (Gershwin)

Solitude

Gone, Gone, Gone from *Porgy And Bess*

Blues In The Night (My Mama Done Tol' Me)

Harlem Nocturne

Black Coffee

The Big Walk

Bluesette

Georgia On My Mind

That Ole Devil Called Love

Quince

When Sunny Gets Blue

Blues Stay Away From Me

Popular Classics

All By Myself

Skater's Waltz (Waldteufel)

Yesterday

Lullaby (Brahms)

Rondo in D Minor from *Abdelazer* (Purcell)

If My Friends Could See Me Now
from *Sweet Charity*

Air On The 'G' String (Bach)

Diamonds Are A Girl's Best Friend
from *Gentlemen Prefer Blondes*

Minuet in G (Beethoven)

Can't Help Lovin' Dat Man from *Show Boat*

Für Elise (Beethoven)

Big Spender from *Sweet Charity*

(Everything I Do) I Do It For You

As Time Goes By from *Casablanca*

Prelude Op.28, No.7 (Chopin)

Every Breath You Take

Humoreske (Dvořák)

Everybody's Talkin' from *Midnight Cowboy*

Fernando

Arthur's Theme from *Arthur*

Wise Publications
London/New York/Paris/Sydney/Copenhagen/Madrid/Tokyo

£14.95

Exclusive Distributors:
Music Sales Limited
8/9 Frith Street,
London W1D 3JB, England.
Music Sales Pty Limited
120 Rothschild Avenue,
Rosebery, NSW 2018,
Australia.

Order No. AM967901
ISBN 0-7119-8551-0
This book © Copyright 1998, 2000 by Wise Publications

Music arranged by Stephen Duro
Music processed by Allegro Reproductions
Cover design by Chloë Alexander
Photographs courtesy of Redferns/Rex
Printed in the United Kingdom by
Printwise (Haverhill) Limited, Suffolk.

Your Guarantee of Quality
As publishers, we strive to produce every book to the highest
commercial standards.
This book has been carefully designed to minimise awkward
page turns and to make playing from it a real pleasure.
Particular care has been given to specifying acid-free, neutral-
sized paper made from pulps which have not been elemental
chlorine bleached. This pulp is from farmed sustainable forests
and was produced with special regard for the environment.
Throughout, the printing and binding have been planned to
ensure a sturdy, attractive publication which should give years
of enjoyment.
If your copy fails to meet our high standards, please inform us
and we will gladly replace it.

Music Sales' complete catalogue describes thousands of titles
and is available in full colour sections by subject, direct from
Music Sales Limited. Please state your areas of interest and send
a cheque/postal order for £1.50 for postage to: Music Sales
Limited, Newmarket Road, Bury St. Edmunds, Suffolk IP33 3YB.

www.musicsales.com

Part One
Jazz Standards

Bernie's Tune

By Bernie Miller

Moderately bright

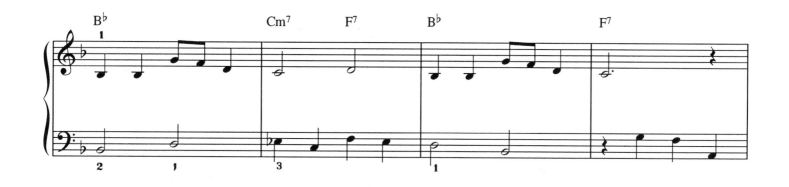

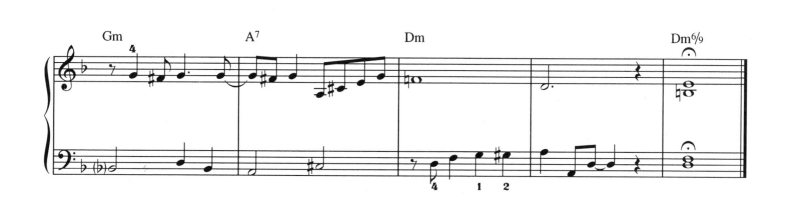

Caravan

By Duke Ellington, Irving Mills & Juan Tizol

Moderately

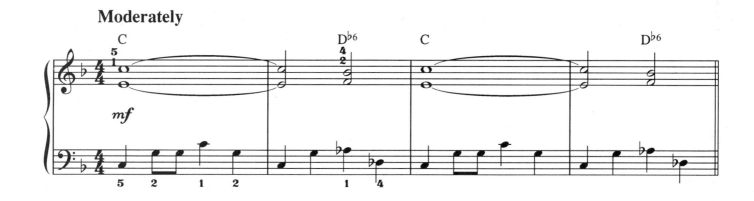

I Wish I Knew How It Would Feel To Be Free

Words by Billy Taylor & Dick Dallas • Music by Billy Taylor

Mood Indigo

Words & Music by Duke Ellington, Irving Mills & Albany Bigard

It Don't Mean A Thing (If It Ain't Got That Swing)

Words by Irving Mills • Music by Duke Ellington

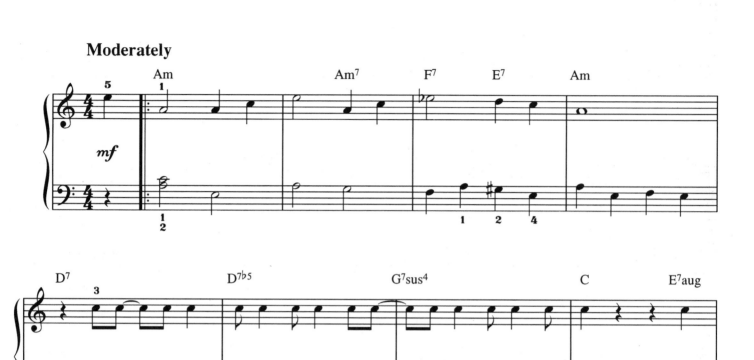

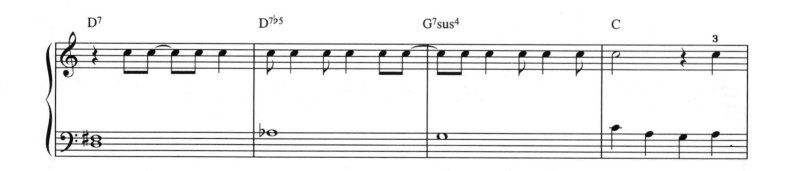

Pennies From Heaven

Words by John Burke • Music by Arthur Johnston

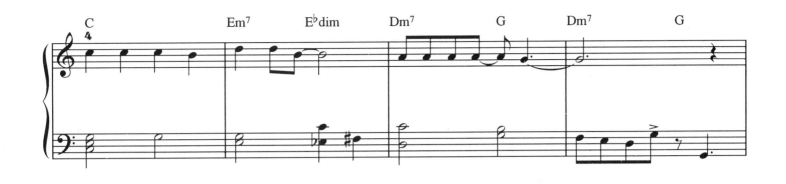

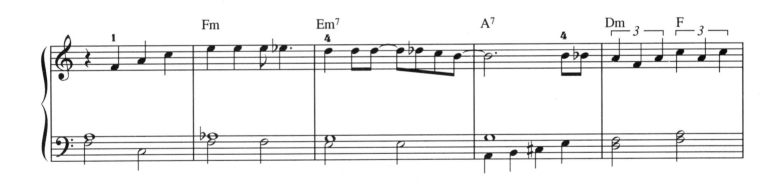

15

Tequila

Words & Music by Chuck Rio

Walkin' Shoes

By Gerry Mulligan

Moderately

Fly Me To The Moon (In Other Words)

Words & Music by Bart Howard

East Of The Sun (And West Of The Moon)

Words & Music by Brooks Bowman

24

Lullaby Of Birdland

Music by George Shearing • Words by George David Weiss

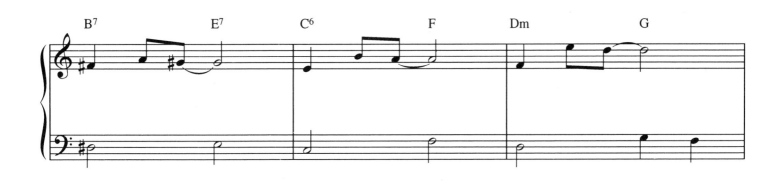

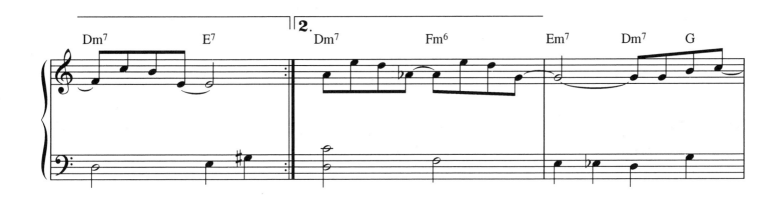

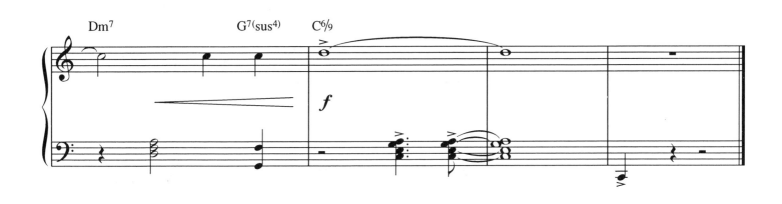

Perdido

Music by Juan Tizol • Words by Harry Lenk and Ervin Drake

Lover Man (Oh Where Can You Be)

Words & Music by Jimmy Davies, Roger Ram Ramirez & Jimmy Sherman

In A Sentimental Mood

Words & Music by Duke Ellington, Irving Mills & Manny Kurtz

33

Satin Doll

Words by Johnny Mercer • Music by Duke Ellington & Billy Strayhorn

35

36

Stella By Starlight

Music by Victor Young • Words by Ned Washington

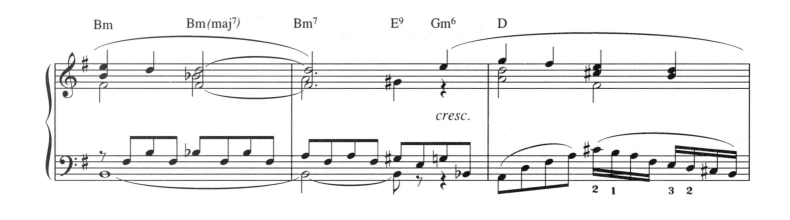

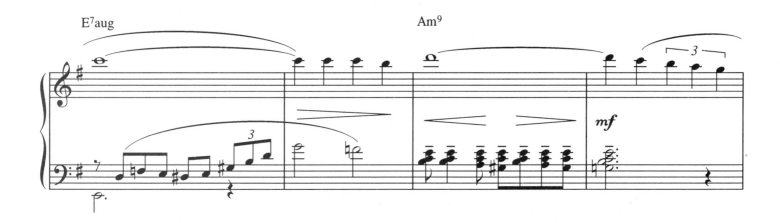

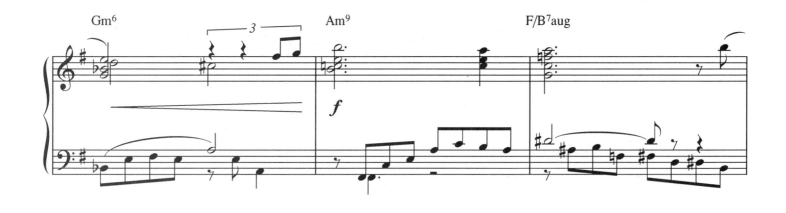

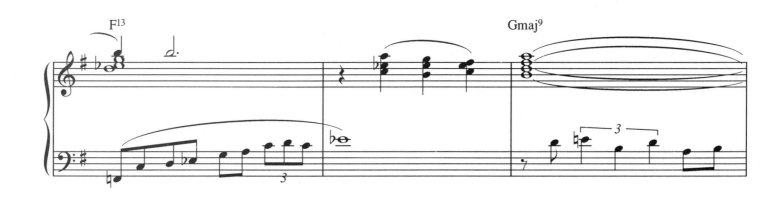

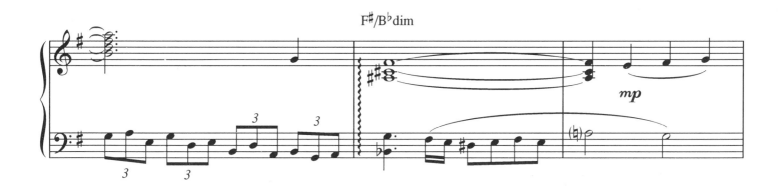

F#/B♭dim

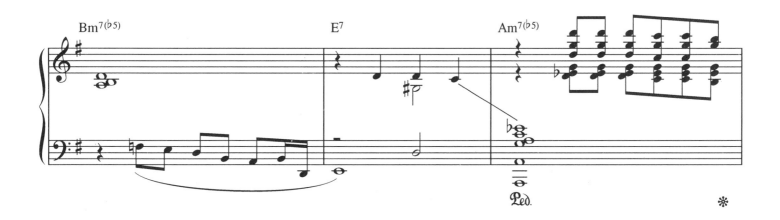

Bm^{7(♭5)}　　　　　E⁷　　　　Am^{7(♭5)}

Ped.　　　　　　　　　　※

B　　Gmaj⁹

delicatissimo

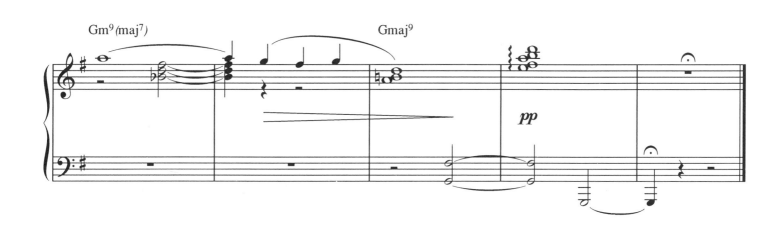

Gm⁹(maj⁷)　　　　　　Gmaj⁹

pp

You Brought A New Kind Of Love To Me

Words & Music by Sammy Fain, Irving Kahal & Pierre Norman Connor

41

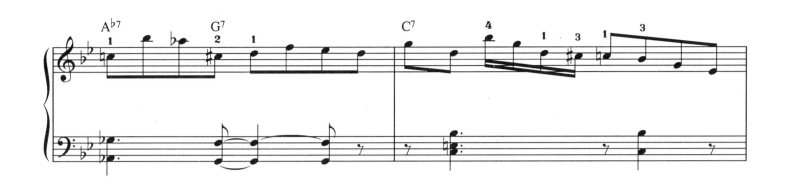

D.S. al Coda

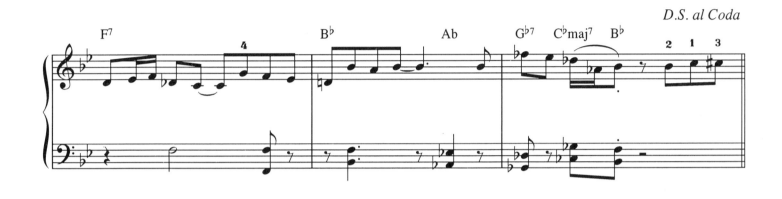

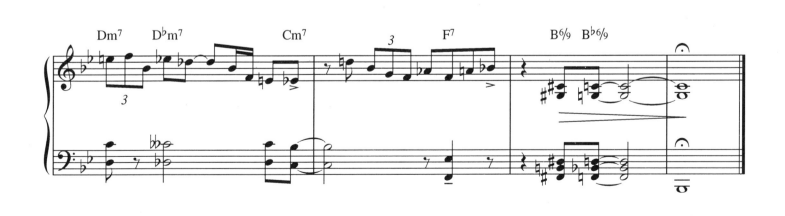

I'll Remember April

Words & Music by Don Raye, Gene de Paul & Patricia Johnson

Moderately bright

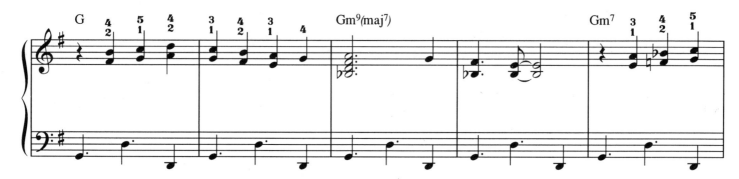

46

Part Two
Blues Greats

Basin Street Blues

Words & Music by Spencer Williams

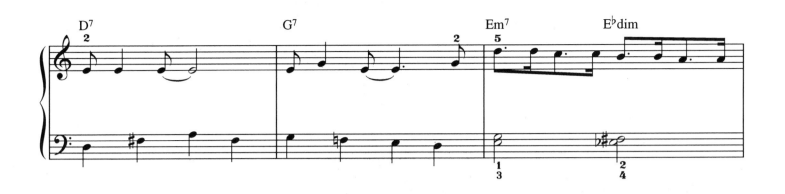

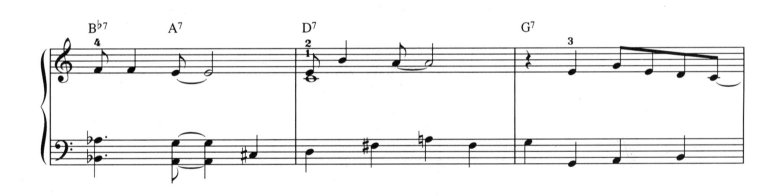

The Man I Love

Music & Lyrics by George Gershwin & Ira Gershwin

Moderately

Angel Eyes

Words by Earl Brent • Music by Matt Dennis

Moderately slow

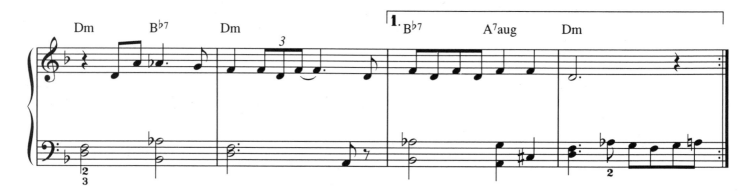

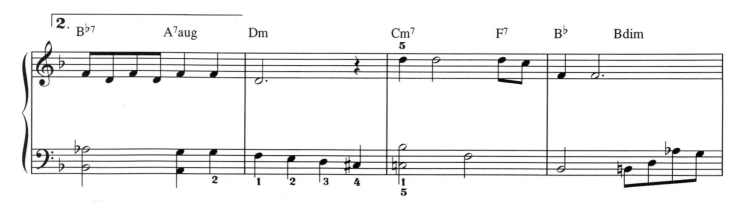

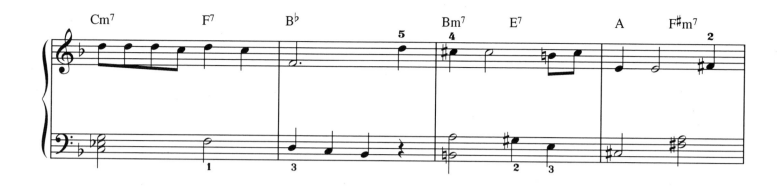

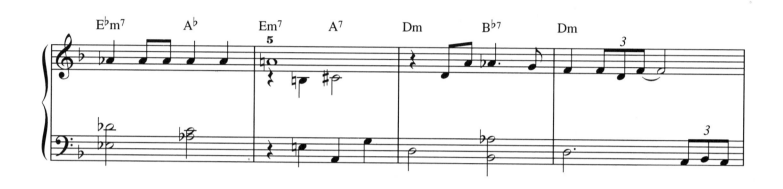

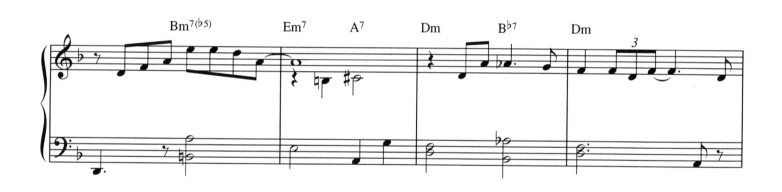

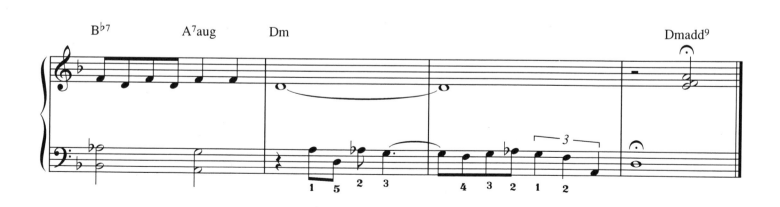

Swingin' Shepherd Blues

Words by Rhoda Roberts & Kenny Jacobson • Music by Moe Koffman

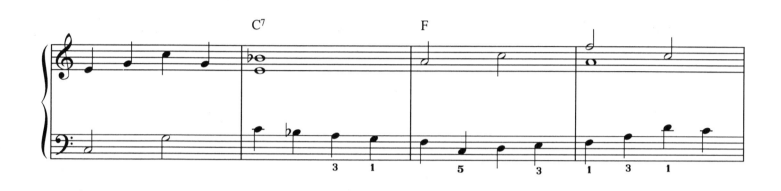

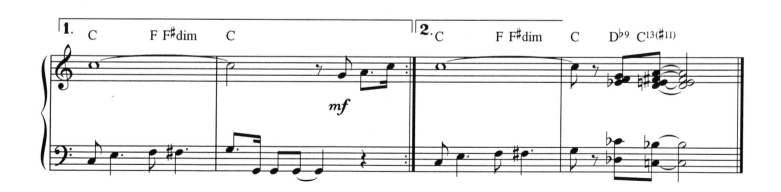

Things Ain't What They Used To Be

Words by Ted Persons • Music by Duke Ellington

Prelude No.2

By George Gershwin

Moderately slow

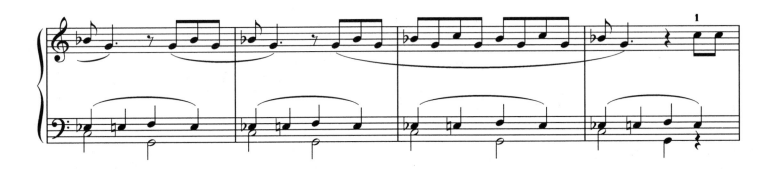

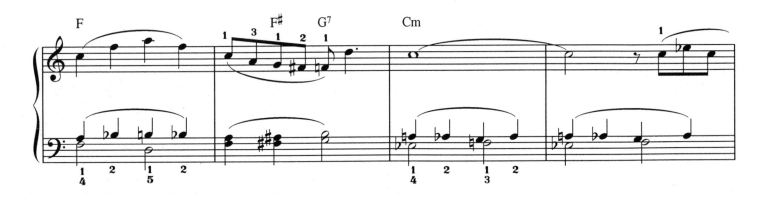

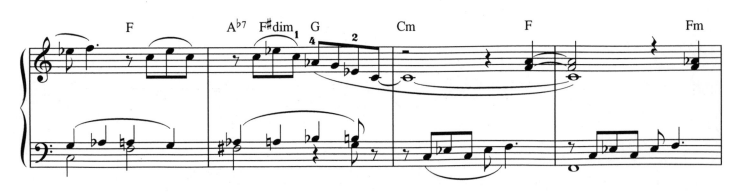

Solitude

Words by Eddie de Lange & Irving Mills • Music by Duke Ellington

Gone, Gone, Gone

from *Porgy And Bess*

Words & Music by George Gershwin, DuBose & Dorothy Heyward & Ira Gershwin

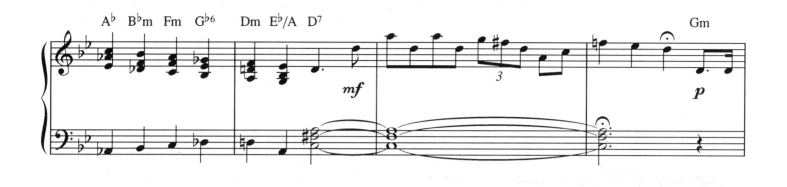

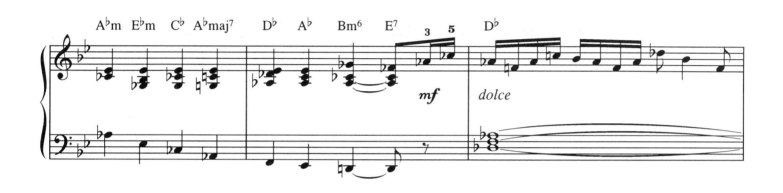

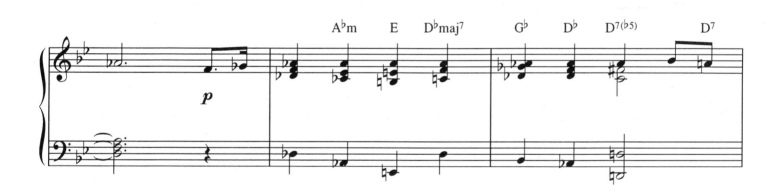

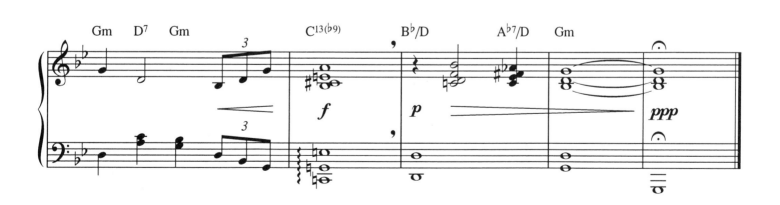

Blues In The Night (My Mama Done Tol' Me)

Words by Johnny Mercer • Music by Harold Arlen

21

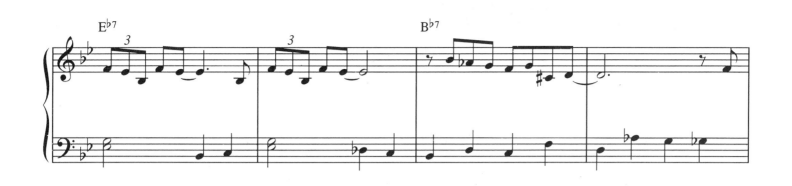

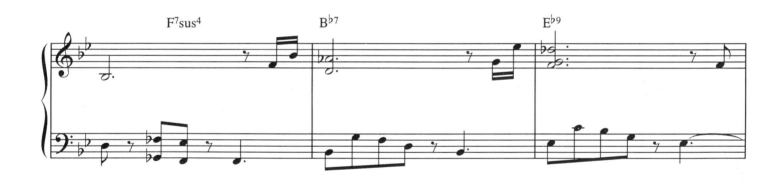

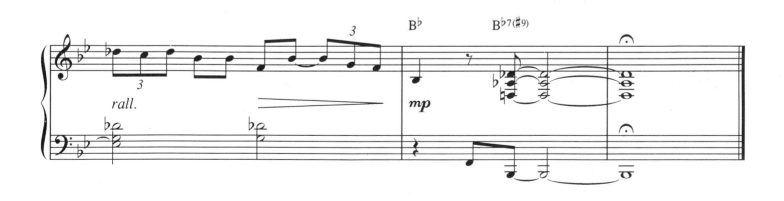

Harlem Nocturne

Music by Earle Hagen • Words by Dick Rogers

Black Coffee

Words & Music by Paul Francis Webster & Sonny Burke

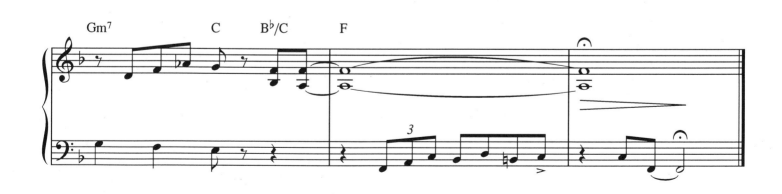

The Big Walk

By Quincy Jones

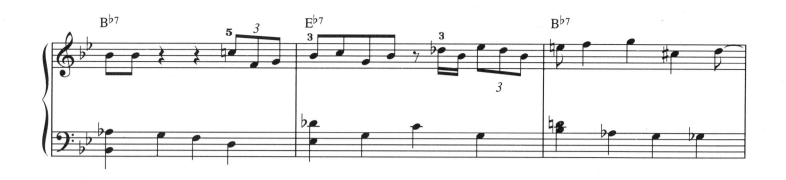

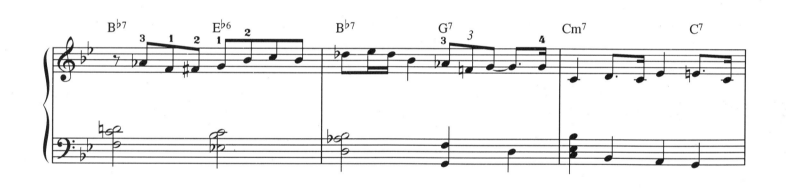

Bluesette

Words by Norman Gimbel • Music by Jean Thielemans

D.S. al Coda

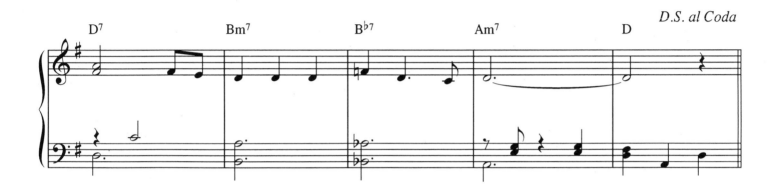

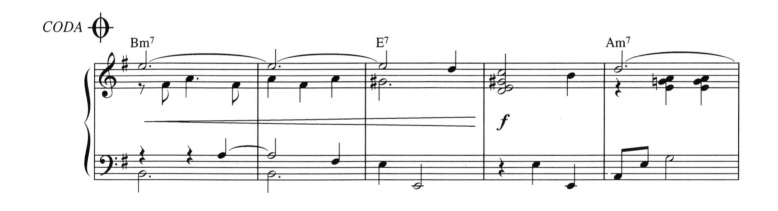

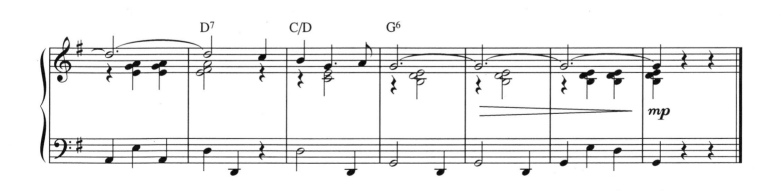

Georgia On My Mind

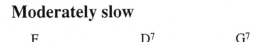

Words by Stuart Gorrell • Music by Hoagy Carmichael

Moderately slow

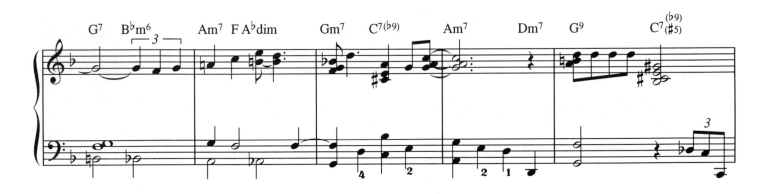

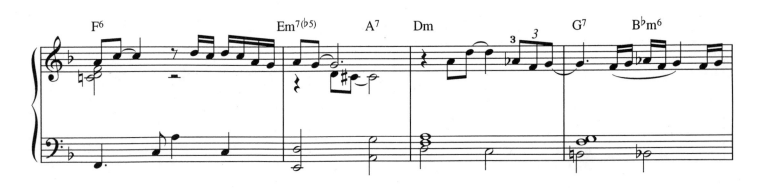

That Ole Devil Called Love

Words & Music by Doris Fisher & Allan Roberts

Quince

By Sonny Stitt

When Sunny Gets Blue

Words by Jack Segal • Music by Marvin Fisher

47

Blues Stay Away From Me

Words & Music by Wayne Raney, Henry Glover, Alton Delmore & Rabon Delmore

Part Three
Popular Classics

All By Myself

Words & Music by Eric Carmen

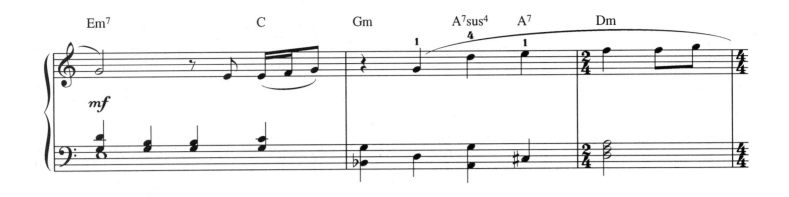

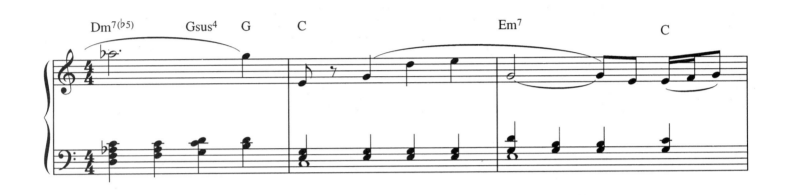

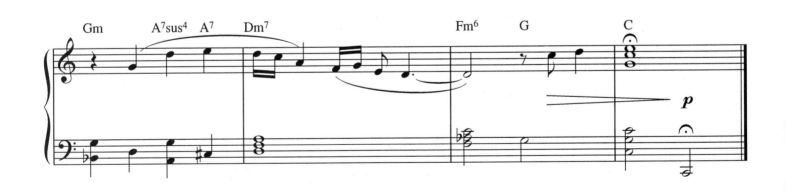

The Skater's Waltz

Composed by Emile Waldteufel

Yesterday

Words & Music by John Lennon & Paul McCartney

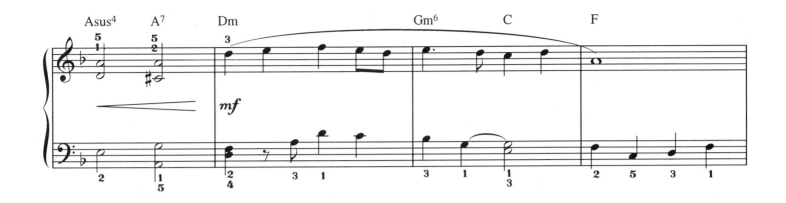

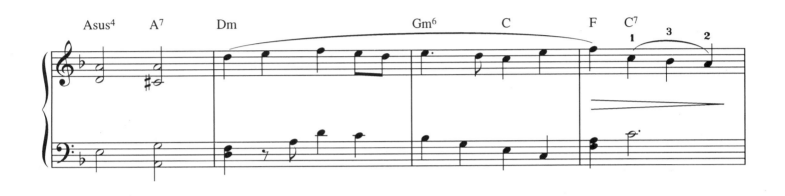

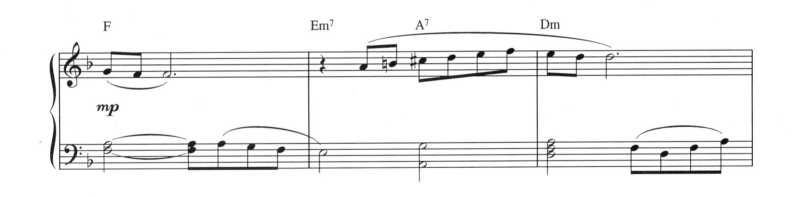

Lullaby

Composed by Johannes Brahms

Moderately slow

Rondo in D Minor

Composed by Henry Purcell

If My Friends Could See Me Now

Words by Dorothy Fields • Music by Cy Coleman

Air On The 'G' String

Composed by Johann Sebastian Bach

Diamonds Are A Girl's Best Friend

Words by Leo Robin • Music by Jule Styne

17

Minuet in G

Composed by Ludwig Van Beethoven

Can't Help Lovin' Dat Man

Music by Jerome Kern • Words by Oscar Hammerstein II

PolyGram Music Publishing Limited, 47 British Grove, London W4.
All Rights Reserved. International Copyright Secured.

Für Elise

Composed by Ludwig Van Beethoven

Big Spender

Words by Dorothy Fields • Music by Cy Coleman

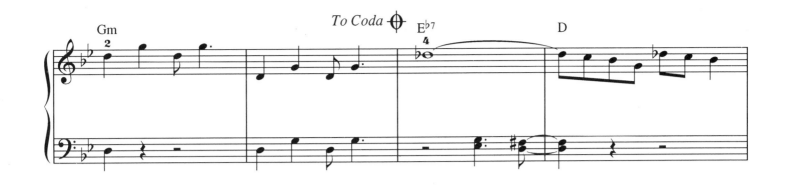

CODA

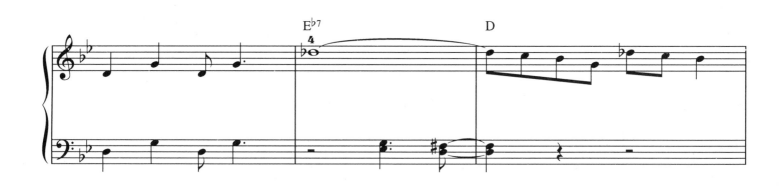

26

(Everything I Do) I Do It For You

Words by Bryan Adams & Robert John 'Mutt' Lange • Music by Michael Kamen

As Time Goes By

Words & Music by Herman Hupfeld

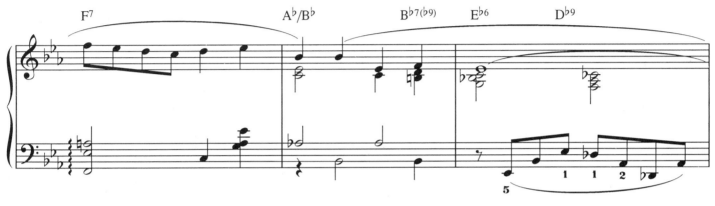

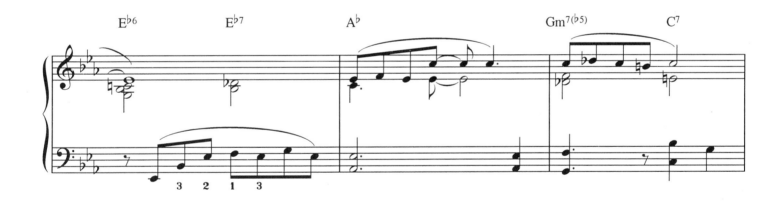

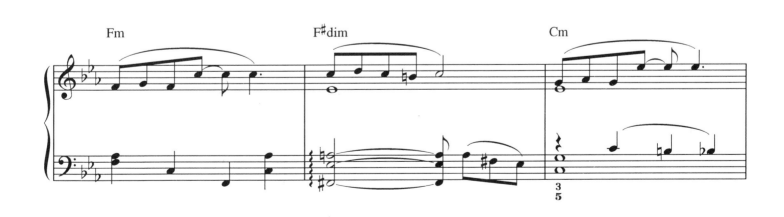

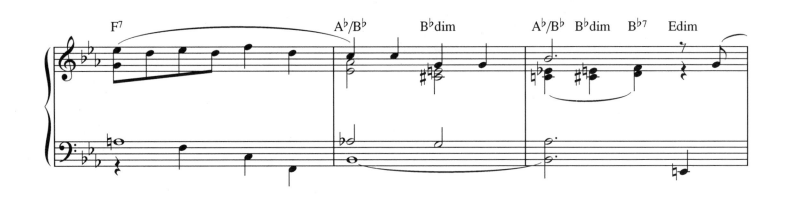

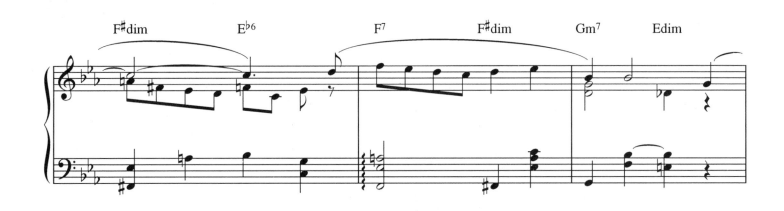

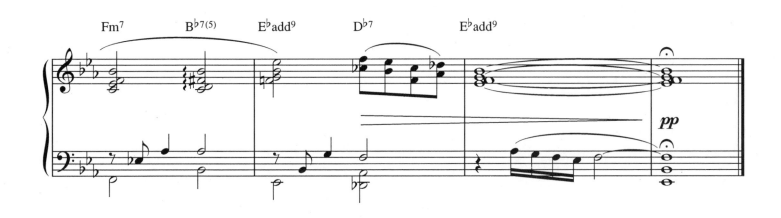

Prelude Op.28, No.7

Composed by Frederik Chopin

Moderately

Every Breath You Take

Words & Music by Sting

Humoresque

Composed by Antonín Dvořák

With movement

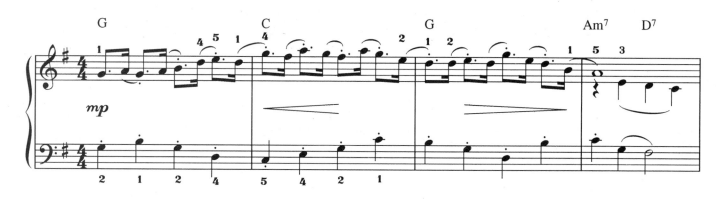

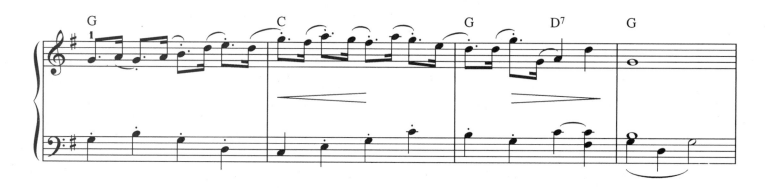

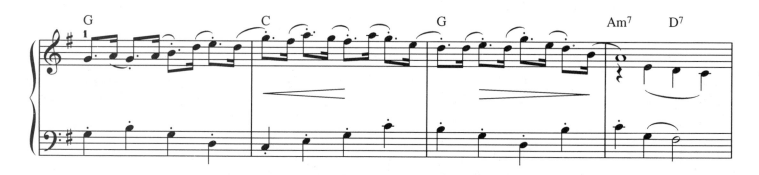

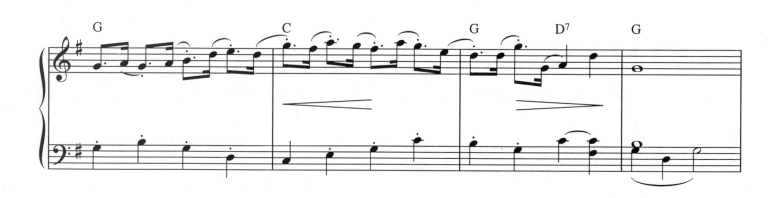

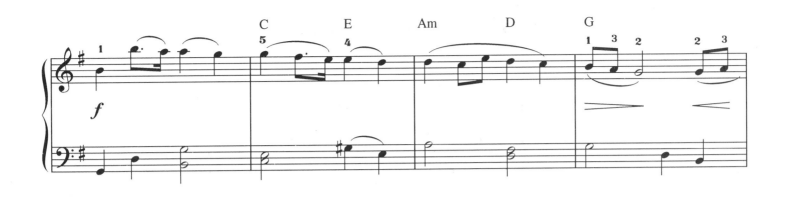

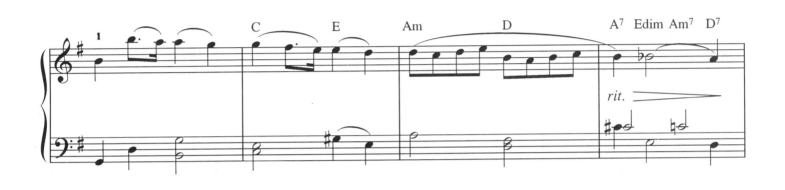

Everybody's Talkin'

Words & Music by Fred Neil

Fernando

Words & Music by Benny Andersson, Stig Anderson & Bjorn Ulvaeus

44

To Coda ⊕

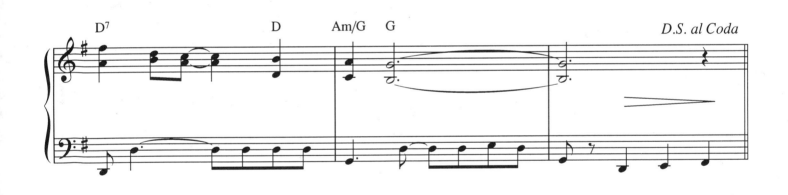

D.S. al Coda

⊕ *CODA*

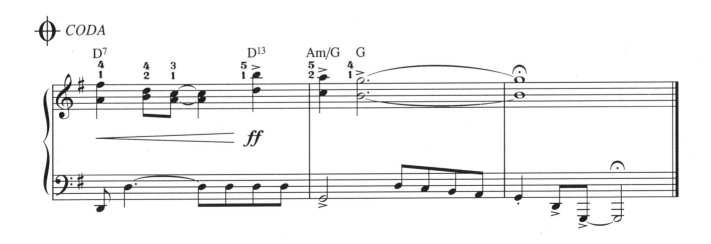

Arthur's Theme (Best That You Can Do)

Words & Music by Burt Bacharach, Carole Bayer Sager, Christopher Cross & Peter Allen

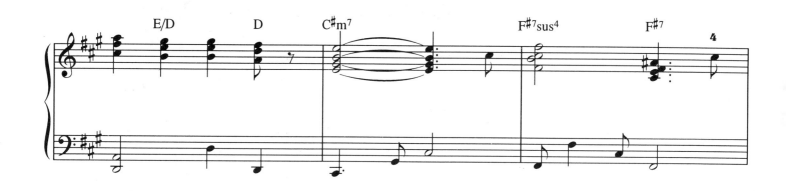